C000270393

Bir
Louth

John Clarkson

Published in association with
Louth Area Group of the Lincolnshire Wildlife Trust
by

Louth Naturalists', Antiquarian and Literary Society

Louth Museum, 4 Broadbank, Louth, Lincs LN11 0EQ
tel: 01507 601211   email: louthmuseum@btconnect.com
2007

© John Clarkson

ISBN 978-0-9539533-5-6

Front cover:
Kingfisher (Graham Catley)

Printed by:
Cupit Print, The Ropewalk, 23 Louth Road, Horncastle, Lincolnshire LN9 5ED

Contents   Page

Preface, Acknowledgements	4
The Survey Area and Map	5
Louth landscapes	7
The Species Account	9
Water Birds	11
Birds of Prey	20
Game Birds	24
Rails and Crane	25
Waders	27
Gulls and Terns	33
Pigeons and Doves	38
Owls	40
Swift, Kingfisher, Roller and Hoopoe	41
Woodpeckers	42
Larks, Hirundines, Pipits and Wagtails	43
Waxwing, Dipper, Wren and Dunnock	46
Thrushes and Chats	48
Warblers	52
Flycatchers	55
Tits	56
Nuthatch, Treecreeper and Shrikes	58
Crows	59
Starlings	62
Sparrows and Finches	63
Buntings	66
Escapes	68
Louth Breeding Birds	69
Reading List and Useful Contacts	75
Index of Common Bird Names	76

Preface

This is not a field guide to the birds of Louth. It is a list of the birds recorded in and around the town, their status and distribution. A recommended identification guide is included in the bibliography.

Acknowledgements

I am grateful to all contributors who have given their time and energy to record the birds of Louth and for allowing me access to those records.

In particular I am grateful to Keith Atkin whose contribution to Lincolnshire ornithology is of the highest order and whose painstaking recording of birds around the town is a model for us all. My thanks also to Steve Lorand, co-author with Keith of *The Birds of Lincolnshire and South Humberside* (1989) and Anne Goodall, co-author of *The Status of Birds in Lincolnshire 1991-1995*, again with Keith: their meticulous research informs much of this work.

I should like to thank the following for providing records and for going out into the field to collect the information used in this book: Norman and Mary Abel, Paul Bennett, Michael and Carol Chevins, Barry Clarkson, Carl Dodge, Phil Espin also for his help in writing the Louth Landscapes section and his generous financial support, Albert Hammond, Roger Labbett, John Loft, the late Lenten Ottaway, Colin Morgan, Sue Morgan, Rita Mortimer, Adrian Royle, Martin Sizer, Mike Tarrant, Steve Tarrant, Nicola Watkins for her support, proof reading and financial support and anyone else who has stopped me in the street and shared with me their enthusiasm for birds. David Robinson deserves special mention for his support of this project, for his expert knowledge of publishing and his constructive and helpful comments.

The Survey Area

At first glance Louth would seem like an easy area to define but this has not been the case. When I asked local people their views about the limits of the town I received a surprising number of answers. One suggestion was the historical Parish of Louth boundary but this has been superseded by development and usage. Another suggested the area within the round Louth walk but this is determined by availability of footpaths. A radius of, say, 2 miles (3 km) from the town centre seemed sensible but it included some outlying villages which I had hoped to avoid as it would invite the question; why stop there? Keddington, being so close to the town, is the one exception.

In the end I plumped for an area more or less covered by a published street plan, as it included the amenity areas apart from the current refuse tip. The survey area is shown in fig.1. This has been overlaid with a grid representing OS 1 Km squares. In essence the map covers those areas where local birdwatchers might walk or cycle or regularly visit and still feel that they are attached to the town. Thus Ticklepenny Lock, Cow Pasture Wood, Kenwick Park Hotel, the Refuse Tip, Raithby Lake and the major part of Stewton Lane are all included.

In the end it seemed more like a consensus than a compromise. The birders I spoke to on this matter all agreed with the area chosen, which, though arbitrary, was based on field experience.

The approximate area covered

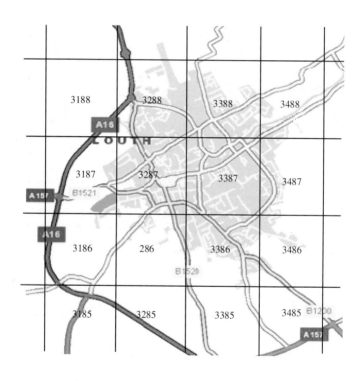

Louth Landscapes

Louth is an historic Lincolnshire market town (pop c 15,000) which straddles the Greenwich Meridian at 58° 22´ N in the valley of the River Lud between the chalk Lincolnshire Wolds and the boulder clay Middle Marsh, about 11 miles from the North Sea.

The Wolds rise to around 95 metres to the west of the town commanding wide views over the Marsh to the sea. These areas are mainly arable with large fields and low hedges. To the west of the town the valley of the River Lud, a chalk water stream has cut into the Wolds producing the attractive steeply wooded valley of Hubbard's Hills. South from there lies Raithby Lake which was formed in the early 1970s in the valley bottom by damming a tributary stream of the River Lud near the disused Louth to Bardney railway line. Below the Hills the river valley opens into pastures and parkland in Westgate Fields and the adjoining Golf Course, Thorpe Hall and Deighton Close. This parkland character continues into the west side of the Georgian heart of the town along Crowtree Lane, St Mary's Lane and Westgate towards St James's Church, which with its 296 feet steeple is the highest parish spire in England and forms our most prominent landmark.

Industry in the town developed along the River Lud particularly with the opening of the Louth Navigation Canal which joined Louth to the sea at Tetney in 1770. There were formerly canal wharves at Riverhead and a series of locks, the lowest to the east at Ticklepenny is around 10 metres above sea level. The Lud valley provides the only two significant open water bodies in the town at Raithby Lake and disused trout ponds on the north side of Westgate Fields. The river and the canal are central to the history of the town, its commerce and its nature. A walk along these watercourses from Raithby Lake to Ticklepenny Lock may produce fifty bird species for the diligent observer at any time of the year.

From the town centre, which has numerous buildings with pantile roofs dating back to the 18th century (attractive for breeding swifts), Louth has spread primarily to the north, where there are modern light industrial estates with landscaped areas, and residentially during the 20th century to the east and south which provide a typical suburban landscape, of housing estates with schools, sports fields, gardens, small greens, allotments and a cemetery.

Although the railways are now long gone, their former lines (where they have not been integrated into building developments and farmland) provide attractive ribbons of scrub with mature trees that are very attractive for birds. The farmland to the north, south and east of town on the Middle Marsh is generally arable with most hedges and permanent pasture fields having been removed for intensive farming or built on and not very productive for breeding birds. In winter and during passage, proximity to the coast, means that interesting birds can and do occur.

The town's old refuse tips which tended to be in quarries have been filled in and built on but retain interesting vestiges of woodland. The most recent at Hungry Corner on the London Road is now a running track with rank wet grassland. The current tip, now nearing the end of its useful life, the former Kenwick Top chalk quarry, is the main attraction for scavenging gulls. To the south east of the town lies Kenwick Park, an attractive wooded parkland which now has a golf course.

These diverse habitats encourage a wide range of birds to visit and reside within the boundaries of Louth. Let us hope that the town maintains this diversity and continues to attract the variety of birds noted in the following pages.

The Species Account

The following pages list all the wild birds known to have occurred within the Louth survey area, a total of 176. The order will be familiar to anyone who regularly dips into a field guide. They are divided, as far as possible into family groups. The first name is the commonly accepted English form. This is followed by the scientific name, in *italics*, which comprises two parts, the generic name, written with an initial capital letter and the specific name.

e.g. **House Sparrow** *Passer domesticus*

The species account is in two broad parts. The first section *in italics* describes the bird's status in Lincolnshire including, where appropriate, frequency of occurrence, breeding status and distribution, extreme dates and recent trends. This information comes from Atkin and Lorand (1989) and Atkin and Goodall (2000). The second section focuses on the status of each species within the Louth area. This includes a summary of trends and details of each sighting in the case of rarer birds, with the initials of the observer included where known. The information for this section has been compiled from published records in Lincolnshire Bird Reports and from the contributions made by local observers.

It will be evident that some names and places occur frequently, such as Keith Atkin and Hazel Grove. It is not that the site is especially good for birds but that the observer has kept records for that locality since 1975. Keith's records show what may be seen by the diligent observer.

It should be noted that the records have been accepted in good faith. Few are so rare that they need the scrutiny of county or national rarities committees and hardly any would be considered contentious. In a few cases the author has discussed identification criteria of some birds with the observer and been satisfied that their submissions are accurate.

Those sightings which are rare in the context of Louth, with fewer than five records, have the name or initials (in the case of regular contributors) of the first known observers after the record. Every effort has been made to identify the finder of the bird but this attribution has not been available in a number of cases, especially where the record has been extracted from Lincolnshire Bird Reports and the bird is not rare in the context of the county.

Contributors mentioned in the species account

KA	Keith Atkin
BMC	Barry Clarkson
JRC	John Clarkson
PE	Phil Espin
CJF	Chris Feare
GH	Graham Hardy
RL	Roger Labbett
JL	John Loft
CLO	Lenten Ottaway
KR	Keith Robinson
AR	Adrian Royle
ACS	Andy Sims
MJT	Mike Tarrant
ST	Steve Tarrant

The Photographers

I am most grateful for the photographs generously supplied by Graham Catley, Barry Clarkson, Dean Eades, Roy Harvey and Mike Tarrant. The remainder are the author's.

Water Birds

Red-throated Diver *Gavia stellata*
Fairly common offshore passage migrant and winter visitor Aug-May. Rare inland and in summer.
There is just one Louth record at Riverhead 9th Feb 1957 (CLO).

Little Grebe *Tachybaptus ruficollis*
Fairly common resident, passage migrant and winter visitor.

Mike Tarrant

A regular winter visitor mainly at Raithby Lake, the old Westgate trout farm pond and occasionally at Riverhead, Hubbard's Hills and Kenwick Golf Course where it has bred. It has been recorded singing at Raithby Lake and may have bred there.

Red-necked Grebe *Podiceps grisegena*
A rare/scarce passage migrant and winter visitor, mainly Sept-Apr.
The sole Louth record is of one stranded in snow 1st Feb 1979 (CLO).

Cormorant *Phalacrocorax carbo*
A common winter visitor, mainly coastal but with increasing numbers inland and in summer. It has bred recently in the south of the county.

Dean Eades

Seldom recorded in Louth owing to the lack of large bodies of water. It has been seen perching on St James's Church and 2 flew over Hazel Grove on 16th Oct 1984. Nineteen flew S there on 22nd Oct 2000. One flew west over on 21st July 2004 and one was at Raithby Lake 24th July 2004. Small numbers have been more frequent over the last ten years but often not recorded.

Shag *Phalacrocorax aristotelis*
A scarce winter visitor to the county.
Only one Louth record. On 27th Jan 1984, whilst driving home, Paul Bennett found one walking along the Brackenborough Road in dense fog. He took it into care and released it at Covenham Reservoir the following day. On 29th there were 6 Shags there and a dead immature bird.

Bittern *Botaurus stellaris*
Formerly a familiar resident of the Fens but drainage and habitat reclamation led to its demise as a breeding species by the mid 1900s. Since then mainly a winter visitor with occasional breeding. However, in the last few years it has re-established itself as a breeding bird at two sites.
There is one Louth record of a brief winter visitor at a pond in the corner of a field near Julian Bower 6th Feb 2004 (JL).

Grey Heron *Ardea cinerea*
A fairly common resident, partial migrant and winter visitor.
A regular visitor locally throughout the year. It is a frequent visitor to Raithby Lake, where there were 12 on 6th July 1982, and other secluded waters and may occasionally be seen at garden ponds. Herons may frequently be seen flying over the town.

Mute Swan *Cygnus olor*
Fairly common and widespread resident and partial migrant.
It is relatively rare in Louth. A 1936 photograph by Dorothy Barker shows a pair and 4 cygnets in Hubbard's Hills. An injured bird was released at Riverhead where it has remained from 2002-2005 and occasional records come from Raithby Lake. Seven flew SE after dark in Oct 2003 and pairs are occasionally seen in flight over the town.

Roy Harvey

Bewick's Swan *Cygnus columbianus*
Fairly common passage migrant and winter visitor, mainly Oct-Mar.
The only Louth record is of 13 flying SE over Hazel Grove 19th Dec 2000 (KA).

Whooper Swan *Cygnus cygnus*
A regular passage migrant and winter visitor to the county, especially on the coast.
The only local records are of 40 which flew E over Hazel Grove on 19th Feb 1997 (KA) and 15 which flew S over Lee St calling on the evening of 25th Nov 1999 (JRC).

Bean Goose *Anser fabalis*
Rare/scarce winter visitor, mainly coastal Oct-Apr.
There is one local record of nine birds of the more
distinctive, larger and longer-necked race *A f fabalis* Taiga
Bean Goose flying easterly low over the town on 30th Oct
2004 (AR).

Pink-footed Goose *Anser brachyrhynchus*
A common winter visitor to the Humber and the Wash with
regular coastal and inland movements.
Flocks are regularly seen flying over the town during the
autumn and winter. Two were with Greylags in fields near
Raithby Lake 2003.

Greylag Goose *Anser anser*
Formerly a common resident in the Fens up to about 1800.
Now a scarce winter visitor, which is difficult to detect
amongst the increasing numbers of feral birds.
Flocks of up to 200 are occasional seen at Raithby Lake and
smaller numbers are regular at this site where they have
bred.

John Clarkson

Canada Goose *Branta canadensis*

Originally introduced from North America in the 18th and 19th centuries to private parks and lakes, and now a common resident and feral breeding species. Frequently recorded at Raithby Lake where it may have bred and fairly regular in flight over the town. Over recent years it has bred successfully at the old Trout Farm lake and Thorpe Hall grounds.

John Clarkson

Barnacle Goose *Branta leucopsis*
Scarce winter visitor Oct-May mainly coastal. Some summer records probably refer to escapes.
One at Raithby Lake from Oct to Nov 2003 with Greylags was possibly an escapee from a collection (JRC).

Shelduck *Tadorna tadorna*
A common coastal and estuarine breeding species.
There are only two local records: a pair flew over (date not recorded) (KA) and a pair were at Raithby Lake 23rd April 2004 (JRC).

Mandarin *Aix galericulata*
Rare/scarce feral resident and visitor. Increased numbers in recent years aided by local release.
There are three Louth records: a drake was at Riverhead 1st May 2002 (Carl Dodge) and another at Raithby Lake 25th May 2004 (JRC) and a female was in Hubbard's Hills 8th June 2004 (AR).

Mallard *Anas platyrhynchos*
Very common resident, passage migrant and winter visitor.
The most numerous and widespread duck in the county.
Well-known in Louth at Hubbard's Hills, Riverhead and along
the course of the Lud where 330 have been counted in
winter; also noted for frequent traffic disruptions during the
breeding season.

Shoveler *Anas clypeata*
Fairly common resident and passage migrant.
The only local record is of 4 at Raithby Lake on 1st Nov
1983.

Wigeon *Anas penelope*
A common winter coastal visitor and passage migrant, which
has rarely stayed to breed.
Small numbers are annual at Raithby Lake in the winter.

John Clarkson

Gadwall *Anas strepera*
A scarce resident and fairly common winter visitor to inland waters with sporadic breeding mainly in Fenland rivers and drains. Has increased in recent years.
A pair were on the River Lud 5th Mar 2002 and a pair were at Raithby Lake 5th May 2003, where there have been up to eight in the winter. Two pairs were present throughout the Spring and early Summer of 2004 but there was no evidence of breeding.

Teal *Anas crecca*
Scarce resident, common passage migrant and winter visitor.
It is regular at Raithby Lake in autumn and winter where up to 100 have been recorded although fewer than 10 is more usual.

Graham Catley

Pochard *Aythya ferina*
A scarce resident and common winter visitor.
There are few Louth records, mainly from Raithby Lake where they are occasional winter visitors. One flew over Hazel Grove on 23rd Jan 1999 (KA) and single birds have been noted on Kenwick Golf Course ponds, also in winter.

Tufted Duck *Aythya fuligula*
A fairly common breeding species and common winter visitor.

Dean Eades

Small numbers are present throughout the year at Raithby Lake where they breed. A few are occasionally noted at the old trout farm in Westgate Fields where breeding might have been attempted and a pair has summered at Riverhead.

Scaup *Aythya marila*
A scarce passage migrant and winter visitor.
One was at Raithby Lake 1st Nov 1976 (CLO) and an immature male was at Riverhead 13th Feb 1986 (BMC).

Long-tailed Duck *Clangula hyemalis*
A scarce winter visitor.
An immature male was at Raithby Lake on 5th Jan 2000 (KA).

Common Scoter *Melanitta nigra*
Fairly common passage migrant and winter visitor on the coast but rare inland.
There is one Louth record of two drakes at Raithby Lake in Jan 1976 (PE).

Goldeneye *Bucephala clangula*
A fairly common winter visitor.

Dean Eades

There have been few local records, with single birds at Raithby Lake; 19th Feb and 12th Nov 1979, 1st Nov 1983, at Kenwick Park a female from 20th Nov to 7th Dec 2000 from 18th to 23rd Feb 2001 and a pair from 8th to 25th Mar 2001.

Goosander *Mergus merganser*
A fairly common passage migrant and winter visitor to inland waters.
A female was at Raithby Lake 18th Jan 1987, 2 flew E over Hazel Grove on 8th Dec 1998 (KA) and a male was at Raithby Lake on 1st Jan 2004 (PE, JRC).

Raithby Lake

John Clarkson

Birds of Prey

Honey Buzzard *Pernis apivorus*
A scarce passage migrant, mainly in autumn.   Extreme dates: 27th Apr - 27th Oct.
There have been two Louth records with one flying west over Kenwick Top 14th Aug 1999 (SDT) and another seen over Kenwick Road (SDT) and Lee St (JRC) 20th Sept 2000.

Red Kite *Milvus milvus*

Roy Harvey

Vagrant occurring in most months though mainly winter to spring. A recent increase is mainly due to introduced birds.

There is one Louth record from 16th Mar 1991 (CJF).

Marsh Harrier *Circus aeruginosus*
Scarce passage migrant and summer visitor, rare in winter. Bred to 19th century when it succumbed to drainage of its main breeding habitat and persecution, then again in 1962 and regularly from 1983; increasing steadily and spreading to several new areas.
There are two Louth records; one flew SE over Hazel Grove on 4th May 1995 (KA) and an adult male flew S over the War Memorial on 6th May 2005 (BMC).

Hen Harrier *Circus cyaneus*
*Scarce passage migrant and winter visitor mainly Sept-May,
occasional in summer. Bred to 1872 when habitat drainage
and persecution brought about its demise.*
The only Louth record is of one flying S over fields near
Brackenborough Rd 9th April 1985 (KA).

Montagu's Harrier *Circus pygargus*
*A scarce passage migrant and an increasingly regular
breeding bird around the Wash.*
A first summer ringtail/female flew N at Raithby Lake 27th
June 1989 (JRC) and another flew S over Lee St on 8th July
2001 (JRC).

Goshawk *Accipiter gentilis*
A rare vagrant, becoming more regular
One was shot in Louth Dec 1830 and subsequently
preserved in Grantham Museum. One seen catching young
pheasants was trapped near Louth on 29th April 1910. A
male flew W over Hazel Grove 21st Aug 1998, an adult male
flew E there on 6th June 1999 (KA) and a male was over
Westgate Fields on 2nd Sept 2004 (JRC, AR).

Sparrowhawk *Accipiter nisus*

Roy Harvey

*Fairly common resident and
passage migrant. Formerly a
common breeding species until
wiped out in the late 1950s by
chlorinated hydrocarbon pesticides.
It has recovered remarkably and is
again a fairly common breeder.*

It is seen frequently around the
town. A female has regularly
roosted on St James's spire over
the winter from 2001 to the present
using the vantage point to hunt
pigeons. Breeds close to town.

Buzzard *Buteo buteo*
Persistent persecution by gamekeepers resulted in its extinction by the end of the 19th century. Fortunately it has re-established its status as a regular breeding bird.
It is now regularly seen over the town, mainly passage birds in spring and autumn, but it has bred within a few miles of Louth at Welton-le-Wold, probably at S. Elkington, and one or two pairs are resident at Haugham and Burwell Woods,

Rough-legged Buzzard *Buteo lagopus*
Rare/scarce passage migrant and winter visitor
One flew over Louth 10th Feb 1996 (GH).

Osprey *Pandion haliaetus*
Scarce passage migrant with occasional summer records.
There is a single Louth record of one between Kenwick Park and the old quarry/rubbish tip 11th Oct 1988 (KA).

Kestrel *Falco tinnunculus*

Mike Tarrant

Common resident and passage migrant. This species suffered a similar fate to the Sparrowhawk in the late 1950s and early 60s but has recovered to its former status as a common resident.
It is regularly seen hovering over fields, open ground and roadsides at the edge of town where it breeds.

Merlin *Falco columbarius*
A scarce passage migrant and winter visitor.
There are eighteen town records, all between Sept and March with most records being from the E side of the town where birds have been seen hunting low over the housing estates and nearby fields.

Hobby *Falco subbuteo*
Scarce summer visitor and passage migrant. Extreme dates: 20th Jan - 25th Oct. This was another formerly regular and widespread summer visitor and breeding raptor, which was persecuted to the point of extinction by the end of the 19th century. It has steadily recovered since the 1970s and is now a regular breeding bird.

Louth records are: one over Kenwick Wood 23rd May 1982, one over Stewton Lane 9th July 1987, one over Legbourne Road 13th June 1990, one over Conscience Hill 25th June 1990, one over Lee St was seen to take a Swift 7th Aug 2000 and another flew over there on 25th July 2003. One took a Swift over the cattle market on 1st Aug 2004.

Peregrine *Falco peregrinus*
A scarce passage migrant and winter visitor. Regular on the coast in winter and in recent years on Lincoln Cathedral. A pair bred in the N of the county in 2003.
There is just one Louth record, 29th Nov 1993 over Deighton Close (JRC).

Game Birds

Red-legged Partridge *Alectoris rufa*
Introduced to Britain in the 1770s and now a common resident.
Occasionally seen in fields around the town and visiting adjacent gardens.

Grey Partridge *Perdix perdix*
Fairly common resident, which has declined noticeably in recent years. This is a national trend, which is most probably due to changes in agricultural methods.
It is occasionally seen in fields near Louth where it has bred.

Roy Harvey

Quail *Coturnix coturnix*
Scarce summer visitor Apr-Sept increasing in recent years and now probably a regular breeder in the Wolds.
The only local record is from Kenwick Golf Course where a male was singing and displaying in 2004 (RL).

Pheasant *Phasianus colchicus*
A very common feral resident.
Resident in the rural edges of town but often seen in gardens.

Rails and Crane

Water Rail *Rallus aquaticus*
A scarce resident and winter visitor, which is probably under-recorded because of its secretive habits.
Individuals are occasionally recorded along the River Lud in winter. An unusual record came from Colin Morgan who found one on his landing in Gospelgate in April 1980, which entered through his bathroom window, and one was at a garden pond in Hazel Grove 5th April 1992 (KA).

Graham Catley

Coot *Fulica atra*
Common resident, passage migrant and winter visitor. A widespread species which requires deeper more extensive water that the Moorhen.
It has been recorded at Raithby Lake where it breeds and occasionally at the old trout farm pond in Westgate Fields where it bred in 2000 and perhaps in 2004.

Moorhen *Gallinula chloropus*
Common and widespread.
Resident along the River Lud and Canal where up to 60 have been noted in winter. Birds may occasionally be seen at very small garden ponds.

John Clarkson

Crane *Grus grus*
Vagrant, recorded most months. A former breeding bird in the Fens now only seen rarely on passage but more frequently in recent years.
An adult flew low N over Hazel Grove 29th April 2000 (KA).

Waders

Oystercatcher *Haematopus ostralegus*
Very common coastal migrant and winter visitor and a fairly common resident.
The only town record is of one that flew over Hazel Grove with Lapwings on 4th Jan 1993 (KA).

Little Ringed Plover *Charadrius dubius*
Summer visitor and scarce breeding bird since 1950. Extreme dates: 7th Mar - 29th Nov.
One was on the Fairfield Industrial Estate 18th July 1980 (BMC).

Ringed Plover *Charadrius hiaticula*
Fairly common resident and common passage migrant, mainly coastal. Breeding has spread to inland sites in recent years.
There is one undated Louth record of a bird in a field on the Brackenborough Rd.

Golden Plover *Pluvialis apricaria*
Very common passage migrant and winter visitor.
Small numbers may be seen flying over, usually in autumn.

Barry Clarkson

Grey Plover *Pluvialis squatarola*
Common passage migrant and winter visitor.
One was on the Abbey Road football ground 22nd Sept 1978 (BMC).

Lapwing *Vanellus vanellus*
Common resident and passage migrant and winter visitor. Breeding numbers have declined in recent years.
Regular in the fields surrounding Louth and occasional flocks over.

John Clarkson

Dunlin *Calidris alpina*
Very common passage migrant and winter visitor, mainly coastal.
The only record was at Raithby Lake 27th July 2003 (JRC).

Ruff *Philomachus pugnax*
Fairly common passage migrant and scarce winter visitor. Bred to 19th century until fenland drainage destroyed its breeding habitat.
One flew over Hazel Grove 17th Jan 1996 (KA).

Jack Snipe *Lymnocryptes minimus*
Scarce passage migrant and winter visitor.
One was in Westgate Fields 26th Jan 1979 (BMC).

Snipe *Gallinago gallinago*
Scarce/fairly common resident, common passage migrant and winter visitor. Breeding numbers have declined presumably because of habitat loss.
There are about 30 local records from Oct to April but it is likely that many are overlooked. Many areas of suitable habitat have been built over in recent years. Most records are from along the Canal and River Lud up to Raithby Lake. Occasional birds have been seen over Hazel Grove mainly in winter and one was at a pond at the end of Wood Lane on 28th July 2004.

Graham Catley

Woodcock *Scolopax rusticola*
Fairly common resident, passage migrant and winter visitor.
There are several Louth records, all between November and
February, with most flushed from damp wood or thicket on
the west side of town and the course of the old railway.

Whimbrel *Numenius phaeopus*
Fairly common passage migrant, mainly coastal.
Small numbers have been heard flying over town in spring
and autumn, usually at night with a peak count of 20 over
Hazel Grove.

Curlew *Numenius arquata*
*Common passage migrant and winter visitor; scarce and
local breeder.*
Passage birds are occasionally recorded over the town

Redshank *Tringa totanus*
Common resident, passage migrant and winter visitor.
There are three Louth records, all of single birds: Riverhead
20th-21st Feb 1978 and again 15th-19th March (BMC),
Riverhead 18th Feb 1979 (BMC) and at Bryan Hall's Mill 7th
Jan 1986 (JRC).

Dean Eades

Greenshank *Tringa nebularia*
Passage migrant, scarce in spring fairly common in autumn, occasional in winter.
One flew over Hazel Grove 10th July 1983 (KA).

Wood Sandpiper *Tringa glareola*
Passage migrant, usually rare in spring and scarce in autumn.

John Clarkson

One was in Hubbard's Hills 3rd-13th Oct 1955 (CLO) and one flew over Hazel Grove 4th Aug 1964 (KA).

Green Sandpiper *Tringa ochropus*
Fairly common autumn passage migrant, scarce in spring and also regular in winter.
There are seven local records, all of single birds: by the Canal E of town 8th April 1989, Hazel Grove 31st Dec 1995, Ticklepenny Lock 3rd Jan 2003, Raithby Lake 27th July 2003, Kenwick Golf Course 1st Apr 2004, Raithby Lake on 24th July 2004 and again near Ticklepenny Lock during the winter 2006-7.

Common Sandpiper *Actitis hypoleucos*
A common passage migrant in autumn and in smaller numbers in spring.
There are eight Louth records, all of single birds as follows: Raithby Lake 22nd May 1975, Charles St by R. Lud 9th Aug 1979, Bryan Hall's Mill 15th Aug 1983, Ticklepenny Lock 16th Aug 1987, one feeding in a gutter in Hazel Grove no date, Raithby Lake 10th May 1990, Raithby Lake 27th July 2003, 24th July 2004 and one there on 25th June 2006.

Turnstone *Arenaria interpres*
Fairly common/common passage migrant and winter visitor. Scarce inland.
The only Louth record is of a single bird at Riverhead 3rd Jan 1996 (KR).

John Clarkson

Hubbard's Hills viewed from the north entrance

Gulls, Terns and Auks

Black-headed Gull *Larus ridibundus*
Common resident, passage migrant and winter visitor.
Non-breeding birds are fairly common around Louth throughout the year. This species, like the other commoner gulls are often seen flying over the town from the tip and surrounding fields to roosting sites on the coast and at Covenham Reservoir.

John Clarkson

Common Gull *Larus canus*
Very common passage migrant and winter visitor.
Not uncommon in Louth - comes to gardens and open spaces such as school playing fields.

Lesser Black-backed Gull *Larus fuscus*
A common passage migrant in spring and autumn, summer visitor and an increasing number of winter birds.
Small numbers may be seen at Kenwick Top Tip throughout the year and occasionally in surrounding fields or in flight towards roosting areas at Covenham Res or on the coast. One or two may rarely be seen at Raithby Lake.

Herring Gull *Larus argentatus*
Very common passage migrant and winter visitor.
One of the commonest large gulls at the rubbish tip, where up to 300 have been recorded. Up to 40 have been recorded at Raithby Lake. Many fly over the town from the tip to roosting sites.

John Clarkson

Great Black-backed Gull *Larus marinus*
Very common passage migrant and winter visitor with some immatures remaining in summer.
The other common large gull; considerable numbers may be seen flying over the town from the Kenwick Top Tip, where up to 350 have been recorded, to roosting sites. Up to 75 have been noted around Raithby Lake.

Glaucous Gull *Larus hyperboreus*
Scarce passage migrant and winter visitor.
All local records come from the refuse tip where there was a 2nd winter bird 2nd Jan 1980 (BMC), a 1st winter bird from 2nd to 11th Jan 1980 (JRC, BMC), another 1st winter bird 1st Feb 1980 (BMC), a 1st winter bird 31st Dec 1991 (JRC) and another 1st winter was there on 13th Jan 1997 (SDT).

Iceland Gull *Larus glaucoides*
Rare passage migrant and winter visitor.
There have been two Louth records both of 1st winter birds at the refuse tip on 6th Mar 1993 (JRC), 9th Jan 1998 and 10th-11th Feb 2006 (BMC, MJT).

Common Tern *Sterna hirundo*
Fairly common summer visitor and passage migrant; most breeding colonies are inland mainly at gravel pits. Extreme dates: 19th Mar - 4th Nov.

The only town record is of 5 SW over Lee St on 25th Aug 2003. (JRC)

Dean Eades

Arctic Tern *Sterna paradisaea*
Fairly common passage migrant, mainly coastal but with some inland passage in spring. Extreme dates 11th April - 4th Nov.
There is one town record of 4 over Church St 3rd May 1998. (JRC, ACS)

Black Tern *Chlidonias niger*
Fairly common passage migrant from spring to autumn. Formerly bred in the Fens before drainage with the last breeding record in mid 19th century. Extreme dates 1st Apr - 10th Nov.

The only local record was at Raithby Lake 28th Sept 1982 (JRC).

Guillemot *Uria aalge*
Fairly common passage migrant and winter visitor but can occur in any month. Rare inland.

The only Louth record is of one on 21st Jan 1963 (CLO).

Little Auk *Alle alle*
Scarce passage migrant and winter visitor. Occasional inland especially after severe weather.

The only Louth record was of one at Acthorpe Top 20th Feb 1979 (CLO).

John Clarkson

The old Louth to Bardney railway line

Pigeons and Doves, Cuckoo and Parakeet

Rock Dove *Columbia livia*
Common and widespread resident.
Feral birds breed at St James's, the Market Hall and the Malt Kiln.

Stock Dove *Columba oenas*
Common resident but shyer and more localized in agricultural areas than the Woodpigeon.
It breeds in more rural areas of town and flocks may be seen in winter. 48 were in one flock at Keddington 2nd Mar 1980 and 40 were noted near Raithby Lake Jan 2004.

Woodpigeon *Columba palumbus*
Very common resident and partial migrant.

John Clarkson

Common in all agricultural and wooded areas of our locality and a regular garden breeding bird.

Collared Dove *Streptopelia decaocto*
Very common resident which has increased dramatically since first recorded in the 1950s.
A common garden bird throughout the town. The table below shows the number of pairs/territories in each 1km square of the survey area in 1997, a total of 457 pairs; a remarkable total for a bird which was unknown here 50 years ago (KA).

0	17	73	44
2	64	86	34
3	28	86	25
2	0	1	5

Dean Eades

Turtle Dove *Streptopelia turtur*
An increasingly uncommon summer visitor.
It might have bred locally and there have been records in the breeding season in suitable habitat such as Stewton Lane, the old East Lincolnshire and Bardney railway lines and Raithby Lake but none in recent years.

Cuckoo *Cuculus canorus*
A common summer visitor, which has declined in recent years. Extreme dates: 4th Apr - 25th Oct.
A regular summer visitor in the rural edges of town where it parasitizes its host species, but more often heard than seen.

Barry Clarkson

Ring-necked Parakeet *Psittacula krameri*
Occasional vagrant from feral populations though some records may be of escaped birds.
One flew over Louth County Hospital on 9th Jan 1991 (BMC, MJT).

Owls

Barn Owl *Tyto alba*
Fairly common resident and partial migrant.
Not uncommon over the fields and roadsides around Louth.

Graham Catley

Little Owl *Athene noctua*
Fairly common feral resident, which has declined recently.
A pair was formerly resident just west of Hubbard's Hills and a pair used to breed in Stewton Lane.

Tawny Owl   *Strix aluco*
Common resident.
Breeds in mature wooded areas particularly in the west end of Louth and its haunting call may often be heard in town.

Long-eared Owl *Asio otus*
Scarce resident, passage migrant and winter visitor.
The only local record is of one near Raithby Lake 7th Nov 1976 (CLO).

Short-eared Owl *Asio flammeus*
Rare resident and scarce passage migrant and winter visitor, which seems to have declined in recent years.
One flew over St Bernard's Ave autumn/winter late 1970s (KA) and a dead bird was found in Adrian's Close in winter 1977 (PE).

Swift, Kingfisher, Roller and Hoopoe

Swift *Apus apus*
Common summer visitor and passage migrant.   Extreme dates: 18th Apr - 10th Nov.
Common over older parts of Louth where nest sites are available. In 1997 there were an estimated 400 breeding pairs across the town (KA); this figure has diminished markedly as new builds and home improvements prevent access to the roof spaces favoured by this species.

Kingfisher *Alcedo atthis*
Fairly common resident and partial migrant.
Regularly seen along R Lud and Louth Canal where breeding has been noted on several occasions.

Roller *Coracias garrulus*
A rare vagrant with only six county records.
An immature bird was shot at Keddington in Oct 1863 and recorded by T H Allis, and one was seen 'near Louth' on 29th Aug 1901.

Hoopoe *Upupa epops*
Rare passage migrant mainly Apr - Oct.
The only Louth record is of a bird, seemingly uninjured, rescued from the jaws of a cat on Horncastle Rd and taken to Lenten Ottaway, but it later died in captivity 26thAug 1975 (MJT, SDT).

Barry Clarkson

Woodpeckers

Green Woodpecker *Picus viridis*
Fairly common resident and partial migrant.
Recorded regularly, principally in winter and early spring, in
the parkland habitat on the west of Louth.

Great Spotted Woodpecker *Dendrocopus major*
Fairly common resident and partial migrant.

Roy Harvey

It has bred in Hubbard's Hills and is regular in woodland
areas around Deighton Close and Westgate Fields. The
most likely woodpecker to be seen; a frequent visitor to
garden bird feeders.

Lesser Spotted Woodpecker *Dendrocopus minor*
Scarce resident.
There are few local records. One was in Stewton Lane
Mar/Apr 1959, one was reported in Cow Pasture Wood 27th
April 1986 (J Vandrill). A male was in Westgate Fields 6th
May 1986. In 2003 a pair bred at Kenwick Golf Course and
were seen there in 2004.

Larks, Swallows, Martins, Pipits and Wagtails

Woodlark *Lullula arborea*
Scarce resident and passage migrant. Bred in 1959 and from 1984; steadily increasing and spreading.
One was flushed from Wood Lane playing fields and perched in a tree in Sycamore Drive 19th Nov 1991 (KA).

Skylark *Alauda arvensis*
Very common resident, passage migrant and winter visitor. Breeding numbers have declined in recent years.
Still fairly common on farmland around Louth.

John Clarkson

Sand Martin *Riparia riparia*
Common summer visitor and passage migrant. Extreme dates 12th Mar - 20th Nov.
Migrant birds are regularly seen at Raithby Lake and occasionally with Swallow movements over the town.

Swallow *Hirundo rustica*
Common summer visitor and passage migrant. Exceptional in winter but recorded in most months.
More common in outlying, rural parts where it breeds but often noted over built-up areas.

House Martin *Delichon urbica*
Common summer visitor and passage migrant. Extreme dates 25th Mar - 20th Dec.
Fairly common around town but declining as a breeding species as the modern building style no longer affords nests the protection they need and the open areas where they would formally collect mud for nests, and feed, are disappearing.

Tree Pipit *Anthus trivialis*
Fairly common summer visitor and passage migrant. Breeds locally, mainly in W Lincs. Extreme dates 4th Apr - 9th Nov.
One was at Deighton Close briefly 23rd May 1995 (JRC).

Meadow Pipit *Anthus pratensis*
Very common resident, passage migrant and summer visitor.
Breeds in suitable habitat around the town and small wintering flocks are regularly seen in rural parts. Occasionally noted in flight over the town.

Rock Pipit *Anthus petrosus*
Fairly common passage migrant and winter visitor.
One was at Raithby Lake 8th April 1983 (CLO)

Yellow Wagtail *Motacilla flava*
A common summer visitor and passage migrant mainly Apr - Sept but recorded in all months, though exceptional in winter.
Has bred near Ticklepenny Lock and possibly on the Lud south of Hubbard's Hills. Occasionally in flight over the town in spring.

John Clarkson

Grey Wagtail *Motacilla cinerea*
Scarce passage migrant and winter visitor. Formerly a rare breeder, which has become more regular in recent years.

They may be seen almost anywhere along the course of the R Lud and the Canal where they now breed annually and they have also been noted in the town centre, Deighton Close and occasionally in gardens.

Pied Wagtail *Motacilla alba*
Common resident and passage migrant.
A local breeding bird, commonplace about the town especially in winter when roosting flocks congregate in the town centre where up to 200 have been counted roosting on the Co-op supermarket.

Waxwing, Dipper, Wren and Dunnock

Waxwing *Bombycilla garrulus*
Winter visitor and passage migrant. Scarce in most years but may be locally common during large-scale irruptions.

Graham Catley

In Feb 1996 such an irruption brought a flock of up to 80 to the Wood Lane area from which groups were noted in Spire View and Hazel Grove. Other small parties were at North Holme Road, Manby roundabout and Little Lane. Smaller numbers are recorded in most years.

Dipper *Cinclus cinclus*
A rare and irregular winter visitor with less than 40 records most of which are of the continental sub-species the Black-bellied Dipper.
There are six Louth records: one was shot in autumn 1884, one over-wintered 1951-52 and another 1963-64 (CLO); one was seen 15th Feb 1969, one was in Hubbard's Hills 8th Dec 1980 (JRC, BMC) and another was well-watched there in Jan 2002.

Wren *Troglodytes troglodytes*
Very common resident and partial migrant.
Recent mild winters have allowed numbers to grow and this
is now a very common local breeding bird in all habitats.

Barry Clarkson

Dunnock *Prunella modularis*
Very common resident and partial migrant.
An unobtrusive but common breeding bird of gardens and
hedgerows.

John Clarkson

Thrushes and Chats

Robin *Erythacus rubecula*
Very common resident, passage migrant and winter visitor.
A familiar and common species in local parks and gardens.

John Clarkson

Nightingale *Luscinis megarhynchos*
Scarce/fairly common local summer visitor and scarce
passage migrant away from breeding areas. Extreme dates:
10th Apr - 23rd Sept. Recent decline.
The only Louth record is of one in Stewton Lane 18th Aug
1987 (BMC).

Black Redstart *Phoenicurus ochrurus*
Scarce passage migrant and rare and irregular winter visitor.
Rare breeding bird.
There are four local records; a singing male was in town
centre 1st July 1989, one was near the Garden Centre on
Legbourne Rd 7th April 1993 (KA), a female was in Eastgate
18th Oct 1995 (KR) and one was in Lee St 7th Nov 2004
(JRC).

Redstart *Phoenicurus phoenicurus*
Rare summer visitor and scarce passage migrant in spring, fairly common in autumn. Extreme dates: 26th Mar - 10th Nov.
One was seen briefly in a Kenwick Road garden 23rd Sept 1982 (KA, JRC).

Stonechat *Saxicola torquata*
Scarce passage migrant and winter visitor.
One was in a garden in Hazel Grove 23rd Feb 1975 (KA) and a female was on Horncastle Rd 18th Mar 2005 (PE).

Wheatear *Oenanthe oenanthe*
Fairly common passage migrant. Formerly a local breeder.
One was on the railway line S of Stewton Lane in April 1975 (PE). Another was there 28th June and 24th-26th Sept 1980 (BMC), again on 19th April 1990 (BMC), one was seen along Brackenborough Rd (no date) and one off Fanthorpe Lane April 2004 (PE).

Ring Ouzel *Turdus torquatus*
Scarce passage migrant Mar-May and Sept-Nov.

Barry Clarkson

One was found dead in Hubbards Hills 17th Oct 2002 (AR). One was at Kenwick Park 2003 (RL). A male was in a field adjacent to the London Rd allotments 27th-28th Apr 2004 (JRC, BMC).

Blackbird *Turdus merula*
Very common resident, passage migrant and winter visitor.
One of the most common local breeding birds.

Fieldfare *Turdus pilaris*

Graham Catley

Common passage migrant and winter visitor.
Frequently seen wherever there is a food supply especially on the outskirts of town. In hard weather may come to gardens.

Song Thrush *Turdus philomelos*

John Clarkson

Common resident, passage migrant and winter visitor. It has declined markedly in recent years.
Around Louth it is outnumbered by the Blackbird some 20:1.

Redwing *Turdus iliacus*

Common passage migrant and winter visitor.
Often seen with Fieldfares especially on the outskirts of town and, perhaps more frequently than that species may visit gardens in hard weather.

Mistle Thrush *Turdus viscivorus*
Common resident and partial migrant.
This large thrush is fairly common, particularly in the parkland habitat and gardens on the W of town.

Westgate Fields

Warblers

Grasshopper Warbler *Locustella naevia*
Scarce summer visitor and passage migrant, which has declined in recent years. Extreme dates: 6th Apr - 21st Oct.
The only Louth record is of one singing along Stewton Lane in spring 1984.

Sedge Warbler *Acrocephalus schoenobaenus*
Common summer visitor and passage migrant; some decline in recent years. Extreme dates: 1st Apr - 13th Oct.
There are Louth records of birds singing along the old railway line on the E of town in the 1970s and in Stewton Lane and Keddington, both in spring 1984.

Lesser Whitethroat *Sylvia curruca*
Common summer visitor and passage migrant, which has increased in recent years. Extreme dates
Common summer visitor and passage: 2nd Jan - 14th Nov.
A local breeding bird in areas of denser, taller bushes such as the old East Lincolnshire railway line, Raithby Lake and Stewton Lane.

Whitethroat *Sylvia communis*
Very common summer visitor and passage migrant. Has recovered from a near catastrophic collapse in the late 1960s and early 1970s probably due to drought in its wintering quarters. Extreme dates: 26th Feb - 12th Nov.
A breeding species around Louth in scrubby areas and hedgerows with thick undergrowth.

Mike Tarrant

Garden Warbler *Sylvia borin*
Common summer visitor and passage migrant. Extreme dates 1st Jan - 27th Nov.
Probably under-recorded around Louth because of its unobtrusive habits but it has been noted in suitable woodland around the town.

Blackcap *Sylvia atricapilla*
Common summer visitor and coastal migrant. Scarce but increasing as a winter visitor.
Occupies similar habitat to Garden Warbler but more obvious and more widely distributed around the town.

Yellow-browed Warbler *Phylloscopus inornatus*

John Clarkson

Rare or scarce passage migrant Sept-Nov, exceptional inland.
One was found in Ramsgate 4th March 2004 where it remained until 11th (JRC).

Wood Warbler *Phylloscopus sibilatrix*
Rare/scarce passage migrant.
There is one local record from Raithby Lake 18th April 1976
(CLO).

Chiffchaff *Phylloscopus collytbita*
*Common summer visitor and passage migrant. Exceptional
in winter.*
Birds may be heard singing in woodland around town from
March or early April. There is a winter record of one on 5th
Feb 1980.

Willow Warbler *Phylloscopus trochilus*
*Very common summer visitor and passage migrant.
Extreme dates 9th Feb - 10th Nov.*
Fairly common summer visitor heard singing from mid-April.
More widespread than the last species, often favouring
mature hedgerows.

Goldcrest *Regulus regulus*
Common resident,passage migrant and winter visitor.
Not uncommon locally in coniferous and mixed woodland
and ranging more widely in winter. It breeds in some
gardens with suitable habitat, especially in the W of town.

Graham Catley

Flycatchers

Spotted Flycatcher *Muscicapa striata*
Fairly common summer visitor and passage migrant, which has declined significantly in recent years. Extreme dates 26th Apr - 5th Dec.

Barry Clarkson

Formerly a widespread breeding species around Louth but now often difficult to find but small numbers still breed in Westgate Fields and Hubbard's Hills.

Pied Flycatcher *Ficedula hypoleuca*
Passage migrant, mainly coastal, commoner in autumn. Extreme dates 11th Apr - 4th Nov.
There are five Louth records of single birds: 3rd-4th Oct 1962, 17th Aug 1977 and a male in Ramsgate 10th May 1978 (CLO). One was in Hubbard's Hills 10th Sept 2002 (AR) and again there on 19th Aug 2004 (AR).

Tits, Nuthatch, Treecreeper and Shrikes

Long-tailed Tit *Aegithalos caudatus*
*Common resident and partial
migrant. Has increased
significantly in recent years
probably as a result
of mild winters.*
Flocks may be seen most of
the year in mixed woodland,
mature hedgerows, bushy
places and more frequently in
gardens .

Barry Clarkson

Willow Tit *Parus montanus*
*Fairly common and widespread resident, which has declined
in recent years.*
The only regular recent records for Louth have come from
the Raithby Lake area. Formerly much more frequently
recorded along the courses of the old railway lines and
Canal and occasionally in gardens.

Coal Tit *Parus ater*
Common resident and partial migrant.
Usually associated with coniferous and mixed woods it is
quite numerous around Louth, often coming to bird feeders
in winter.

Blue Tit *Parus caeruleus*

John Clarkson

*Very common resident;
increasing numbers
in recent years.*
A common local
breeding bird which is
well known at bird
feeders throughout
the area

Great Tit *Parus major*
Very common resident with increased numbers in recent years.

Another well-known local bird, a common visitor to gardens and bird feeders.

Nuthatch *Sitta europaea*

Scarce/fairly common local resident mainly in the south-west of the county.

One picked up after crashing into a window at Deighton Close was later released 13th Oct 1993. Probably the same bird was there on 1st Dec and again on 26th Feb 1994 (JRC). One was in Westgate Fields 31st July 2003 and there regularly into summer of 2004 when a pair were noted. These bred and raised at least 2 young (JRC, AR) and have remained in the area, breeding in subsequent years.

Treecreeper *Certhia familiaris*
Common resident in all types
of woodland and partial
migrant.
Elusive but fairly common in
the wooded areas of town,
particularly Hubbard's Hills,
Westgate Fields and adjoining
Areas, including gardens.

Graham Catley

Red-backed Shrike *Lanius collurio*
Scarce passage migrant, mostly on the coast.
One on the Little Cawthorpe Rd flew into Kenwick Park near
the Legbourne Rd junction on 22nd May 1986 (KA).

Great Grey Shrike *Lanius excubitor*
Rare/scarce passage migrant and rare winter visitor Oct-Apr.
Recent decline.
One was recorded 17th Dec 1971 and another flew over
Hazel Grove 21st April 1983 and perched briefly in bushes
and trees either side of the street (KA).

John Clarkson

The River Lud at Bridge Street

Crows

Jay *Garrulus glandarius*
*Common resident especially in the west of the county,
irregular migrant and winter visitor.*

Louth records may
relate to birds of
European origin, which
are subject to periodic
irruptions governed by
the supply of acorns.
One was at Deighton
Close 4th Feb 1980.
There are four records in
1983 of singles at
Deighton Close 17th-19th
Oct, Raithby Lake 1st Nov,
Kenwick Top 1st Nov and
Hazel Grove 19th Dec.
Birds involved in the same
influx stayed into 1984

Graham Catley

when there was 1 in Westgate Fields 5th Jan, 1 Deighton
Close 3rd-5th Jan, 2 there on 6th and 3 on 27th. Birds were
present on Kenwick Golf Course in 2004 where they bred.

Magpie *Pica pica*
Very common resident, which has increased in recent years.
Well known throughout the town where it is a common
breeding bird.

Jackdaw *Corvus monedula*
Very common resident, passage migrant and winter visitor.
Often found alongside other crows in fields and at the refuse
tip. Sometimes breeds in rookeries and also at St James's
and in the chimneys of older properties in town.

Rook *Corvus frugilegus*
Very common resident, passage migrant and winter visitor.
Common in fields on the outskirts of town and at the refuse tip. There are rookeries on Eastgate at the bottom of Church St and in trees by the Manby roundabout.

Barry Clarkson

Hooded Crow *Corvus cornix*
Rare winter visitor and passage migrant.
One was at the refuse tip on 1st and 5th Feb 1980 another there on 15th March 1981 (BMC, MJT) and one was in Hazel Grove perched on a rooftop 31st Oct 1987 (KA).

Carrion Crow *Corvus corone*
Common resident, passage migrant and winter visitor.
Fairly common around town, especially at the refuse tip, breeding in the more rural areas.

Raven *Corvus corax*
Probably a fairly common resident into the 18th century. Now a rare vagrant. A pair arrived in the Grantham area in 2003 and stayed to breed in 2004.
A pair bred on St James's Church 1693, and one flew SW over Hazel Grove 22nd July 2003 (KA).

Starlings

Starling *Sturnus vulgaris*
Very common resident, passage migrant and winter visitor, which has declined in recent years.
A common breeding bird in all parts of the town.

Roy Harvey

Rose-coloured Starling *Sturnus roseus*
A rare vagrant.
There is one Louth record of a well watched adult in gardens in Ramsgate Place 13th-15th June 2001 which was found by Albert Hammond feeding in his garden.

Graham Catley

Sparrows and Finches

House Sparrow *Passer domesticus*
Very common resident and partial migrant, which has declined nationally in recent years.

Still a fairly common local breeding bird but there has been a marked decline across the town.

Tree Sparrow *Passer montanus*
Common resident and partial migrant but there has been a marked decline in recent years.
Most records are from the west of town from Hubbard's Hills to Raithby where they have bred, and occasionally on the north and east of town. The highest counts have been 30 in Jan 1982 and the same in Jan 2004.

Chaffinch *Fringilla coelebs*
Very common resident, passage migrant and winter visitor.
Common across the town in all wooded and garden areas.

Brambling *Fringilla montifringilla*
Common winter visitor and passage migrant.

Graham Catley

Small numbers are regularly noted in late autumn and winter, especially with Chaffinch flocks in Hubbard's Hills and surrounding areas with up to 100 birds recorded. The peak count was of 140+ at Elkington fork 12th Feb 1991.

Greenfinch *Carduelis chloris*
Very common resident, passage migrant and winter visitor. Increase in recent years.
Common throughout the year and a frequent garden visitor.

Goldfinch *Carduelis carduelis*

Barry Clarkson

Common resident and passage migrant.
Probably a fairly common breeding bird across the town. Flocks of up to 50 birds have been noted in fields on the edge of town. Also a frequent garden visitor in the autumn when it feeds on seedheads of teasels and thistles.

Siskin *Carduelis spinus*
Common passage migrant and winter visitor.
Small flocks of up to 30 birds are regular in the alders of Thorpe Hall and may be seen from Westgate Fields. It also visits garden feeders.

Linnet *Carduelis cannabina*
Very common resident, passage migrant and winter visitor.
Fairly common in more rural areas and especially so in the winter. Has bred in most areas of the town.

Barry Clarkson

Common Redpoll *Carduelis flammea*
Increasingly uncommon resident, passage migrant and winter visitor.
Since the 1980s when it probably bred in most areas in and around Louth there has been a dramatic decline and there are now a mere handful of records annually.

Mealy Redpoll *Carduelis cabaret*
Scarce and easily overlooked winter visitor.
An adult male was drinking at a garden pond in Hazel Grove 9th Nov 1990 (KA).

Crossbill *Loxia curvirostra*
Scarce/fairly common irruptive passage migrant and visitor mainly June-April occasionally all year. Only proved to breed on a few occasions.
There are three Louth records, all from Kenwick Park: a male 23rd May 2001, 20 on 30th Aug 2002 and 30 on 31st Dec 2002 (RL).

Bullfinch *Pyrrhula pyrrhula*
Common resident.
Mainly seen in the mature hedgerows along the old railway line, Stewton Lane, Raithby Lake and Hubbard's Hills. It has bred in these areas.

Dean Eades

Hawfinch *Coccothraustes coccothraustes*
Scarce local resident and rare passage migrant.
The sole Louth record is of a bird at the southern end of Hubbard's Hills on 28th Mar 2005 (AR).

Buntings

Snow Bunting *Plectrophenax nivalis*
Fairly common passage migrant and winter visitor on the coast mainly Sept-Apr. Regular but scarce inland.
There is one Louth record of a female on the Stewton Lane railway line Feb 1976 (PE).

Yellowhammer *Emberiza citrinella*
Common resident. Some decrease in recent years.
A bird of farmland, bushy areas and woodland edges. Unusual in urban areas. Most frequently seen between Hubbard's Hills and Raithby Lake. It has bred in several outlying areas of town.

Reed Bunting *Emberiza schoeniclus*
Common resident and passage migrant. Some decline in recent years.
There are surprisingly few Louth records. Most have been in the winter months, visitors to gardens from adjacent farmland. They may have bred along the Canal near Keddington in the 1980s. The only recent records have come from the north end of Fairfield Industrial estate.

Graham Catley

Corn Bunting *Miliaria calandra*
Common resident and partial migrant. Decline noted in recent years.
The only records are of one holding territory in fields between Kenwick Rd and London Rd in 1981 and another in the 1980s in the Grimsby Rd/Industrial Estate area.

Louth Navigation Canal at Keddington Lock

John Clarkson

Escapes

Bar-headed Goose *Anser indicus*
Alpine lakes in central Asia; winters in India and Myanmar.
Fairly common in wildfowl collections.
Two were in a flock of 200 Greylags in a field adjacent to
Raithby Lake 29th Oct 2000 (JRC).

Wood Duck *Aix sponsa*
Canada to N Mexico, Cuba and Bahamas.   Popular in
wildfowl collections.
A drake was at Riverhead 24th June 2000 (KA, HB)

Golden Pheasant *Chrysolophus pictus*
Mountain slopes of central and s China.   Introduced to the
British Isles.
Escapees have been recorded: one was by the old railway
bridge near Bryan Hall's Mill 12th April 1989 (BMC) and a
female was seen at Deighton Close c.1995 (JRC, ACS).

Unconfirmed sighting

White-tailed Eagle *Haliaetus Albicilla*

This is from the diary of Margaret Loft, great grandmother of
John Loft, 18th March 1845. Mr St George was a clergyman
and apparently curate at St James's. Certainly this is a good
date for such a bird. One was in Lincs during Mar 2005.

Louth Breeding Birds

The following pages show the distribution of breeding birds in the survey area comparing the range of birds in the mid 1980s when the author was surveying for the *Lincolnshire Bird Atlas*. Some species, such as Turtle Dove, have declined in line with national trends. Others have declined owing to local developments where modern building methods have drastically reduced the availability of nest sites for Swifts and House Sparrows. Redpolls, which were noted in 50% of the squares in the 1980s were completely absent in 2004. The infill and improvement of derelict and unused areas and the expansion of the town, especially the industrial estate, has reduced the amount of open land but extended the area of the town beyond the survey grid.

The charts show the status of all species suspected of breeding in the survey area. Although the survey area has expanded, the same sixteen squares have been used although some have been 'extended' to include new developments. So, for example 3288 includes the growth of the industrial estate in 3289.

The British Trust for Ornithology uses the following codes to denote the status of breeding birds in their survey work and these were used during both Louth surveys.

Confirmed Breeding (B in table)

DD	Distraction display
FL	Recently fledged young
FY	Feeding young or carrying food to young
NE	Nest with eggs
NY	Nest with young
ON	Occupied nest
UN	Recently used nest

Probable breeding (b in table)

D	Displaying
P	Pair in appropriate habitat
T	Bird holding territory
H	Bird in appropriate habitat
S	Bird singing

For reasons of space these codes have not been used here and tables are annotated with a lower case b to indicate probable breeding and an upper case B to show where breeding has been confirmed.   The black character on the left of each cell shows the status in the 1980s and the red character on the right shows the breeding status in 2004.

3188	3288	3388	3488
3187	3287	3387	3487
3186	3286	3386	3486
3185	3285	3385	3485

3188 - Farmland   **3288** - Fairfield Industrial Estate
3388 - Keddington and Brackenborough Rd, old railway
3488 - Keddington
3187 - Westgate Fields, Deighton Close, Cow Pasture Wood
3287 - Westgate, St Mary's Lane, Old Cemetery, R Lud, town centre
3387 - R Lud, Railway Walk
3487 - St Bernard's Ave., farmland   **3186** – Hubbard's Hills
3286 - Horncastle Rd, London Rd, Julian Bower
3386 –Newmarket, Cemetery, Sports ground
3486 - Stewton Lane, old railway
3185 - Raithby Lake, old railway
3285 - Bypass, footpath from Julian Bower
3385 - London Rd, Kenwick Rd, farmland
3485 - Legbourne Rd, Kenwick Road, Kenwick Park

Species	3485	3385	3285	3185	3486	3386	3286	3186	3487	3387	3287	3187	3488	3388	3288	3188
Little Grebe												b B				
Mute Swan													b		b	
Canada Goose				B	b b							B				
Mallard				B B		b		B B		B B	B B	B b	B B	B B		
Gadwall				b												
Tufted buck				B B				b			b	b				
Sparrowhawk		b		b	b	B b			b	b			b			
Kestrel	b			b	B		B		b		b	b		b	b	
Red-legged Partridge		B B	b	b								b				b b
Grey Partridge		b b	b	b			b	b				b				b
Pheasant	b	B B	b b	b		b	b		b	b		b	b	b	b	B b
Moorhen			b	B B	b		b	B B		B	B B	b b	B B	B B		
Coot			b	B B								B				
Lapwing				b								b			b	b b
Rock Dove	b					b	B	B		b B	B b			b	b	b b
Stock Dove		b		b			b B	B B	b	b b	b b	b	b	b	b	b b
Woodpigeon	b	b b	B	B B	B B	b B	b B	b	b	b B	b b	B b	b	b b	b b	b
Collared Dove	b	b b	b b	b	B B	B B	b	b	b			B b	b b	b	b	b
Turtle Dove					b S										b	

Species	3188	3288	3388	3488	3187	3287	3387	3487	3186	3286	3386	3486	3185	3285	3385	3485
Cuckoo	b	b b			b							b b	S	b		
Barn Owl	B			b		B						b	b			B
Tawny Owl			b	b	B b	b b			b		b	b b	b	b		b
Swift		b b	B B	b b		B B	B B	B B	B B	b	b b	b b	b			
Kingfisher					b B	b b					B B		B B			
Green Woodpecker				b	b b	b			b	b				b		
Great Spotted Woodpecker			b		b				b B	b			b			b
Lesser Spotted Woodpecker																
Skylark	b b	b b	b		b		b	b b				b b	b b	b	b b	b b
Swallow	b b	B B	b B	B B	B B	B B	B		B B	b b	B	B B	B B		b	B B
House Martin	b	B B	b B	B B	B B		B B	B	b B	b B	b B	B B	b			
Meadow Pipit							b	B		b				b		
Grey Wagtail				b		B B	B b		B				b			
Yellow Wagtail							b			b	b					
Pied Wagtail		B	B	B		b			B	B	b	b	b			b
Wren		b	b	b	B B	B B	b B	b	b B	b b	b	b b	b	b	b	b
Dunnock	b	b B	b	B B	B b	b b	b b	b b	b b	b B	b B	B B	b B	b b	b	b
Robin	b	b	b	B B	B B	b b	b B	b	B B	b	b B	B B	b	b b	B B	b
Blackbird	b b	B B	B B	B B	B B	B B	B B	B B	B B	B B	B B	B B	b	b b	b B	b B

Species	3188	3288	3388	3488	3187	3287	3387	3487	3186	3286	3386	3486	3185	3285	3385	3485
Song Thrush	b	B	b	B	B	B	B	b	B	b	B	B	b	b	b	b
Mistle Thrush	b		B	b	B	b	B	b	b	B	B	b	b	b	b	
Grasshopper Warbler												b				
Sedge Warbler				b								b				
Lesser Whitethroat				b	b		b				B	B	b			
Whitethroat	b	B		b			b	b			b	b	B		b	b
Garden Warbler				b						b			b			b
Blackcap	b	b	b	B	b	B	b		b	b	b	b	B	b		b
Chiffchaff				b	B	B	b		b	b	b	b	b	b	b	b
Willow Warbler				B	b	B	b		b	b	b	b	b	b	b	b
Goldcrest			b	b	B	B	b		B	b	b	B	b			b
Spotted Flycatcher	b			b	B		B	b	B	B		B			b	
Long-tailed Tit			b	B				b	b	b		B	B	B		
Willow Tit											b	b	b			
Coal Tit	b		b	b	B	b	b		b	b	b	B	B			b
Blue Tit		B	B	B	B	B	B		B	B	B	B	b	B	b	B
Great Tit	b	B	b	B	b	b	B		B	B	B	B	B	B	b	b
Nuthatch					B											
Treecreeper					b				b	b						

Species	3485	3385	3285	3185	3486	3386	3286	3186	3487	3387	3287	3187	3488	3388	3288	3188
Magpie	B b	b	b	b B	B B	B b	B B	B	b b	B B		b b	B b	B b	B	b
Jackdaw	b		b		b b	B B	B B	B B	b b	B B	B	b	B	b	b	b
Rook	B B					B B		B B		B B	B					
Carrion Crow	B B	b	b	B B	b	B b	B B	B B	b	b b	b	B	b B	b	B	b b
Starling	B b	b b		B	B B	B B	B B	B	B B	B b	B B	B B	B B	B B	B b	b
House Sparrow	B b	b B	b	B B	B B	B B	B B	B b	B B	B b	B b	B b	B B	B B	B B	B b
Tree Sparrow	b				B b			B					b			
Chaffinch	b b	b	b	B b	B b	B B		B B	b	B B	b b	B b	b b	b b	b	b
Greenfinch	b b	b		B	B B	B B	B B	b b	b	b b	b b	b b	B b	b b	b B	b
Goldfinch	b b	B B		b b	b b	B B	b b	b	b	b b	b	b b	b b	b	b B	
Linnet	b			b b	b b	B B		b	b B	b	B b	B b	b		b b	B
Redpoll					b	b		b		b	b	b	b	b		
Bullfinch				b b	B		S	B		B		B b		b		
Yellowhammer	b	b b	b	b	b b	b	b		b				b b		b	b b
Reed Bunting		b b											b		b	
Corn Bunting						b										b

Selected Reading List

Anne Goodall and Keith Atkin (2000) *The Status of Birds in Lincolnshire 1991 - 1995* Lincolnshire Bird Club.
An update to the earlier work of Lorrand and Atkin (1989).

Smith A E and Cornwallis R K (1955) *The Birds of Lincolnshire* Lincolnshire Naturalists' Union, Lincoln
The first full account of the avifauna of Lincolnshire which provided the platform for all subsequent studies.

Stephen Lorrand and Keith Atkin (1989) *The Birds of Lincolnshire and South Humberside* Hawes, North Yorkshire: Leading Edge Press.
A detailed and comprehensive modern account of the county's avifauna.

Cornwallis, R K (edited and revised by K Atkin and A D Townsend) (1970) *Supplement to the Birds of Lincolnshire 1954-1968* Lincolnshire Naturalists' Union, Lincoln

Killian Mullarney, Lars Svensson, Dan Zetterstrom, Peter J. Grant (2000) *Collins Bird Guide* London: Harper Collins.
The best of the modern field guides covering Britain, Europe and N Africa.

Useful contacts

Lincolnshire Bird Club, Secretary, 3 Oxeney Drive, Langworth, Lincoln LN3 5DD. or
www.lincsbirdclub.co.uk

Lincolnshire Wildlife Trust
Banovallum House, Manor House Street, Horncastle, Lincolnshire LN6 5HF or www.lincstrust.org.uk
Tel: 01507 526667

Lincolnshire Naturalists' Union, c/o Lincolnshire Wildlife Trust

Index of Common Names

Arctic Tern	34
Barn Owl	40
Bar-headed Goose	68
Barnacle Goose	15
Bean Goose	14
Bewick's Swan	13
Bittern	12
Black Redstart	48
Black Tern	34
Blackbird	50
Blackcap	53
Black-headed Gull	33
Blue Tit	56
Brambling	63
Bullfinch	65
Buzzard	22
Canada Goose	15
Carrion Crow	60
Chaffinch	62
Chiffchaff	54
Coal Tit	56
Collared Dove	38
Common Gull	33
Common Sandpiper	32
Common Scoter	18
Common Tern	34
Coot	25
Cormorant	12
Corn Bunting	67
Crane	26
Crossbill	65
Cuckoo	39
Curlew	30
Dipper	46
Dunlin	28
Dunnock	46
Fieldfare	50
Gadwall	17
Garden Warbler	53
Glaucous Gull	34
Goldcrest	54
Golden Pheasant	68
Golden Plover	27
Goldeneye	19
Goldfinch	63
Goosander	19
Goshawk	21
Grasshopper Warbler	52
Great Black-backed Gull	34
Great Grey Shrike	58
Great Spotted Woodpecker	42
Great Tit	57
Green Sandpiper	31
Green Woodpecker	42
Greenfinch	63
Greenshank	31
Grey Heron	13
Grey Partridge	24
Grey Plover	28
Grey Wagtail	44
Greylag Goose	14
Guillemot	34
Hen Harrier	21
Herring Gull	34
Hobby	23
Honey Buzzard	20
Hooded Crow	60
Hoopoe	41
House Martin	44
House Sparrow	62
Iceland Gull	34
Jack Snipe	29
Jackdaw	59
Jay	59
Kestrel	22
Kingfisher	42
Lapwing	28
Lesser Black-backed Gull	33
Lesser Spotted Woodpecker	42
Lesser Whitethroat	52
Linnet	64
Little Auk	36
Little Grebe	11
Little Owl	40
Little Ringed Plover	27
Long-eared Owl	40
Long-tailed Duck	18
Long-tailed Tit	56
Magpie	59
Mallard	16
Mandarin	15
Marsh Harrier	20
Meadow Pipit	44
Mealy Redpoll	64

Merlin	23	Shelduck	15
Mistle Thrush	51	Short-eared Owl	40
Montagu's Harrier	21	Siskin	64
Moorhen	26	Skylark	43
Mute Swan	13	Snipe	29
Nightingale	48	Snow Bunting	66
Nuthatch	57	Song Thrush	50
Osprey	22	Sparrowhawk	21
Oystercatcher	27	Spotted Flycatcher	55
Peregrine	23	Starling	61
Pheasant	24	Stock Dove	37
Pied Flycatcher	55	Stonechat	49
Pied Wagtail	44	Swallow	43
Pink-footed Goose	14	Swift	41
Pochard	17	Tawny Owl	40
Quail	24	Teal	17
Raven	60	Tree Pipit	44
Red Kite	20	Tree Sparrow	62
Red-backed Shrike	58	Treecreeper	58
Red-legged Partridge	24	Tufted Duck	18
Red-necked Grebe	11	Turnstone	38
Redpoll	64	Turtle Dove	32
Redshank	30	Water Rail	25
Redstart	49	Waxwing	46
Red-throated Diver	11	Wheatear	49
Redwing	50	Whimbrel	30
Reed Bunting	66	White-tailed Eagle	68
Ring Ouzel	49	Whitethroat	52
Ringed Plover	27	Whooper Swan	13
Ring-necked Parakeet	39	Wigeon	16
Robin	48	Willow Tit	56
Rock Dove	37	Willow Warbler	54
Rock Pipit	44	Wood Sandpiper	31
Roller	43	Wood Warbler	54
Rook	60	Woodcock	30
Rose-coloured Starling	61	Wood Duck	68
Rough-legged Buzzard	22	Woodlark	43
Ruff	28	Woodpigeon	37
Sand Martin	44	Wren	46
Scaup	18	Yellow Wagtail	44
Sedge Warbler	52	Yellow-browed Warbler	53
Shag	12	Yellowhammer	66
Shoveler	16		

Notes

Notes

Notes